C000218755

Glouceste_____ _ _ ___y___

This book is sold in aid of

The Hop Skip & Jump

Play & Support Centre
for children with life-threatening
illnesses or any special needs.

The Centre provides day care facilities and supervised play
for children and young people with physical, emotional and
learning disabilities. This enables their families to have a
break, knowing that their children are safe, enjoying excellent
facilities at an adventure playground where they are supported
by a highly dedicated team.

Hop Skip & Jump Cotswold
(Registered Charity No. 1088173)
Seven Springs, Cheltenham, GL53 9NG

Email: hsj@hsjcotswold.plus.com

Website: www.cotswoldhopskipandjump.org

In association with the
Seven Springs Foundation
(Registered Charity No 1081810)

Gloucestershire Rhymes

by
E.R.P. Berryman

Introduction by Anthony Boden
Music by Charles Lee Williams

c h o s e n

p r e s s

in association with the
Seven Springs Foundation

Published in 2008 by
Chosen Press, Lichfield, Staffordshire
for the Seven Springs Foundation

ISBN 978 0 9556373 9 1

Cover illustration and map by Rolf Jordan

Printed by Cromwell Press, Trowbridge, Wiltshire, Great Britain

CONTENTS

Gloucestershire Rhymes

Introduction

'Oh yes! I remember the Nursery Rhymes of Gloucestershire', said an old friend recently, 'we used to sing some of them at school when I was a little girl; they were lovely'. And like many other people who attended Gloucestershire schools during the 1930s, she will undoubtedly find a reawakening of delight in these charming and inventive verses, now restored to print for the first time since 1984.

It was in 1930 that Gloucester businessman John Fielding told Dr Charles Lee Williams, a former Organist and Master of the Choristers at Gloucester Cathedral, that his son-in-law, Lieutenant Colonel E.R.P. Berryman, had 'put together some simple "Nursery Rhymes" which might be amusing to the school children of Gloucester'. Mr Fielding showed the first dozen or so rhymes to Lee Williams, who immediately became interested, convinced that Berryman's knowledge of Gloucester history and its ancient place-names would not only please the rising generation of children but also cause many adults to 'sit up and take notice'. The two men soon became friends, and in March 1931 Lee Williams published a private edition of nine of the rhymes under the title *Nursery Rhymes of Gloucester City* (printed by John Bellows of Gloucester). Berryman, obviously delighted, wrote to Lee Williams saying 'I sincerely hope you will find time to set some of my efforts to music for the amusement of a larger circle of Gloucester children'. Lee Williams readily took up this suggestion, and his settings of a selection of the rhymes appeared in July 1931 (again printed by John Bellows). Some of the tunes from Lee Williams's settings are included in this new edition of the rhymes; Eileen O'Malley set a further four, which were published by Boosey & Hawkes in 1969; and Johnny Coppin's irresistible modern interpretation of 'Cotswold Tiles' enjoys well-deserved and widespread popularity.

Edward Rolleston Palmer Berryman, always known to family and friends as Ted, was born on 10th July 1883, the third of the thirteen children of the Reverend Charles Berryman and his wife Gertrude. Educated at the King's School Canterbury, Ted went on to the Royal Military College (now Academy) Sandhurst, and by 1913 was serving as an officer in the 39th Royal Garhwal Rifles, Indian Army, based at the regimental depot in Lansdowne, a small hill station in Uttaranchal, 81 kms from Pauri.

At the outbreak of the First World War, in August 1914, the 39th Garhwalis were mobilised for active service and Ted appointed Adjutant of their 2nd Battalion. A vivid description of Berryman's war is to be found in a collection of the family's war letters 1914-1918, edited by Ted's daughter, the late Félicité Nesham, and published in 1987 under the title *Socks, Cigarettes and Shipwrecks* (Sutton Publishing). The letters reveal the extraordinary fortitude and bravery displayed by Berryman, his fellow officers and men after being shipped from India to Europe in September 1914 as part of the Indian Expeditionary Force.

The voyage itself posed a considerable trial to Indian

troops, transported for the first time from the remote hill-country of Northern India. Most of them had never 'seen a ship or a sheet of water bigger than a bucket before [and] were frightfully ill'. They arrived in France at the end of October and three days later were in the trenches, facing mud, rain and freezing conditions in their summer kit.

During those first few weeks, the Garhwalis 'had a good many men killed and wounded', but after a week's rest they returned to the front line, still without warm clothing. Then, on 1st January, Ted was at last able to write home that: 'I've got my new uniform now & have had a bath—in an old dustbin — but still it was a bath, & I feel so clean and smart.'

During March 1915 the Garhwalis played a major role in the capture of Neuve Chapelle, sustaining heavy losses, and in the following May, Captain Berryman was wounded, suffering a gunshot wound to his left leg. He was evacuated to hospital in Wandsworth, recovered for light duties, and in August was ordered to a temporary posting with the 3rd Battalion of the 5th Gloucesters, so beginning a deep attachment to the county celebrated in his rhymes. There was an attachment of another kind, too, when Ted fell in love with one of John Fielding's daughters.

Fielding, a director of a large Gloucester engineering company, Fielding & Platt, lived in an imposing house, 'Broadsground' (now the Hatton Court Hotel), at Upton St Leonards, situated on the hill above the training camp at Sneedham's Green. Like many others at the time, John Fielding and his wife Pauline (*née* Miles) offered hospitality to officers stationed in the neighbourhood. And so it was that Ted came to meet and befriend four of the Fielding children.

There were five girls: Gladys, Marjorie (away on tour at the start of a theatrical and film career), Louie, Nell and Isabel, and a boy, Jack (due to go up to Cambridge to read engineering, but training instead with the Royal Artillery). It was the fourth daughter, Nell, who captured Ted's heart, and on 29th October 1915 the couple became engaged. Nell was only seventeen years old, but, for lovers during war, time is too precious to waste. Ted was soon under orders to rejoin his regiment, and set sail for India aboard the *SS Persia* on 15th December.

Two weeks into the voyage, the *Persia* was torpedoed in the Eastern Mediterranean (one of the 'shipwrecks' in the book title referred to). Ted, caught by a huge rush of water, was carried away from the ship, which sank within five minutes. 'The sea . . . was full of human beings and floating wreckage. Chairs, tables, broken spars and beams were everywhere. The air was full of groans and cries, and everywhere one looked it seemed one saw human beings struggling in the water'. Attempting to swim towards four distant lifeboats, he 'saw a lady lying on her back, apparently utterly exhausted, and just drifting helplessly away'. Ted, taking this poor woman in tow with one hand, and swimming with the other, with his legs continually getting mixed up in her skirts, was, with great difficulty, eventually able to reach a boat containing about forty people.

The exhausted passengers were in their open lifeboats for more than thirty hours before being rescued by a minesweeper, *HMS Mallow*, Ted in the bows comforting one of the two children, 'a little French girl about six' whose questions about 'the big boat coming to rescue us' were 'awfully pathetic'. Only one hundred and fifty passengers survived out of the more than five hundred who had embarked upon *SS Persia*. Ted's action in saving life at sea was recognised in due course and his name was put forward for the bronze medal of the Royal Humane Society.

He finally arrived back in India in March 1916. Of the twenty-six officers who had started out from Lansdowne in September 1914, only six returned, but in March 1917 the 2nd/39th Royal Garhwal Rifles were again called to active duty, this time in Mesopotamia (present-day Iraq). As second in command, Ted was promoted to the acting rank of major, and later to temporary lieutenant colonel—in time to command the Garhwalis, fighting alongside the 1st/5th Queens, in a decisive victory against the Turks at the Battle of Ramadi in September 1917. The Turkish guns captured there still flank the gateway to the Regimental Mess in Lansdowne. The remainder of Ted's war was spent in Mesopotamia, but even when hostilities ended, because he was Indian Army, he did not return directly to England.

He did not arrive back from India until 12 May 1919, and on his arrival at Southampton sent a telegram to his future in-laws:

FIELDING, UPTON ST LEONARDS, GLOS

WATERLOO FIVE O'CLOCK. WHERE'S NELL
WIRE ME JUNIOR NAVAL AND MILITARY CLUB 96
PICCADILLY.
TED

One month later, they were married.

It was whilst he was serving in the Indian Army during the 1920s that Ted wrote that he had been 'trying his hand at writing rhymes for his small son' (Martin). The idea for them came from Nell, who had been reading Eleanor Farjeon's *Nursery Rhymes of London Town*, and suggested that he might do the same for Gloucester by writing about such place names as 'Lady Belle Gate' and 'Barbican Alley', and more rhymes were to follow the birth of his daughter Félicité in 1924.

Before her marriage, Pauline Fielding's family home had been at 'Belmont', a fine house with magnificent views across the Vale of Gloucester, situated near to 'Broadsground' on the hill at Upton St Leonards. Her father Edwin Miles and his family were very close friends of the Fieldings, and when Edwin died in 1915 he left 'Belmont' to Pauline. And so this house, its name changed to 'Edmonds Hill', was to become Ted and Nell Berryman's home when they moved from Surrey to settle in Gloucestershire in 1950; Félicité (now married to another ex-Garhwali officer, Robert Nesham) lived with them, and in due course four grandchildren shared this happy family home. Martin, who had followed his father into service with the Garhwalis (as so often happened in the days of the Raj), had been killed in action in Malaya before he was twenty-one, an enduring sense of loss to all—even to his nephew and nieces, born years after his death.

In 1954 the British Publishing Company Limited of Gloucester printed a collection of thirty-two of Ted's *Nursery Rhymes of Gloucestershire*, branching out from the city limits of the earlier publication into the villages and places around, Hucclecote, the Hatherleys and, particularly, Seven Springs. The book is dedicated 'To Roberta, born in Surrey but who migrated to Gloucestershire at the age of three months.'

> *Surrey may rightly claim that you*
> *By virtue of your birth*
> *Should owe a loose allegiance to*
> *Her soft, sun-dappled earth.*
> *But Time will change that loyalty*
> *When you are older grown,*
> *For surely you will bow the knee*
> *To Cotswold wood and stone.*

In a reprint of the book in 1960 Ted Berryman added an explanatory Foreword:

> The majority of these rhymes, written for my children and grandchildren, are of course purely 'Nursery' in character in that they have no foundation in fact but are just figments of the author's brain. Some, however, have either history or tradition behind them and perhaps a little information on these may be of interest.
>
> Littleworth, for instance, is said to be so called because Charles I during the siege of Gloucester had to abandon a small earthwork when it was attacked but regarded the loss as of little consequence. [F.A.] Hyett, describing the siege in his book *Gloucester in National History* [Gloucester, 1906], chap. vii, says: 'The main attack was directed against the S.E. corner of the city, from a

powerful battery on Gawdy Green. The assailants once effected a breach in the walls but could not effect an entrance.' Hyett also states: 'engineers commenced digging trenches on Gawdy Green (on which Brunswick Square now stands).' The idea that fairs were ever held on Gaudy Green, as stated in the rhyme of that name, is purely fictional.

The origin of the name Oxbode Lane is seemingly lost, but it is hoped that the rhyme about it will help to preserve its correct pronunciation—*Oxbody*. It was, up to the 1920s or thereabouts, a very narrow lane before it was pulled down and the present wide thoroughfare took its place, and perhaps it was then that it lost its real pronunciation, for one hears it generally referred to as The Oxbode, to rhyme with 'mode'.

'Rhyme of a Seven Springer' was inspired by the well-known rival claims of Thames Head and Seven Springs to be the true source of the River Thames. Thames Head, near the village of Coates, is certainly dry for a great part of the summer; people who know about these things say it is a 'winterbourne' and not a perennial spring. The Thames Conservancy in their journal published in 1957—the hundredth anniversary of their formation—admit the existence of the dispute and add 'the actual source of the Thames is not legally or otherwise officially defined, but the view of the Conservators (which has much backing) is that Thames Head is the true source'. So the Seven Springer must remain content with the fact that Seven Springs is only the source of the River Churn, a mere tributary of the Thames.

September 5th, 1643, is the actual day on which Charles I withdrew his army from the siege of Gloucester before the Parliamentary forces under Essex advancing from the Cheltenham direction. The Royalists retired over Painswick Beacon, and John Sawyer in his book *The Story of Gloucestershire* [Cheltenham, 1907] writes (Chap. xliv): 'the relief of Gloucester saved Parliament, but was only a temporary defeat for the King. There is a local tradition that on his way over Painswick Hill one of his sons asked him when they were going home, and that he replied: "I have no home to go to".' The stone from which the King is traditionally supposed to have mounted his horse during the withdrawal is still standing on Cud Hill, near Painswick Beacon, and is marked on the six-inch and other ordnance maps.

As regards the Kings Head at Upton St. Leonards, Canon Scobell in his records of that village writes: 'there is documentary evidence to show that King Henry VIII and Anne Boleyn visited Upton after their coronation and Corporation records show that on August 2nd, 1535, "they rode towards Prinknash to hunting," accompanied by the Mayor and some of his brethren. They appear to have visited an inn named The Harrow, to which the title The King's Head was then given.'

The mention of 'wool churches' in the rhyme 'Port o' Gloucester' refers of course to those built by wealthy wool merchants in the fourteenth and fifteenth centuries, of which Chipping Campden and Northleach are outstanding examples. Such churches sometimes bore marks of the wool trade; for instance, the tower of Cranham church near Painswick has shears carved in stone on it. Most of the wool seems to have been carried to London on pack horses and shipped abroad from there, but doubtless some found its way down the Severn.

The origin of the cheese-rolling ceremonies down Cooper's Hill are certainly lost in the mists of time. Some attribute them to the druids, others to some tradition connected with grazing rights on the common land. Certain it is that nobody really knows, and the suggestion in the rhyme would appear to be as good as any other!

In a 1960 birthday letter to one of his cousins by marriage, Anne Miles, Ted revealed the source of his information for yet another of the rhymes. He enclosed a copy of the recently reprinted edition with his letter, describing it as 'a slight—very slight!—& frivolous gift', and explaining that one of the rhymes—'Gallows Lane'—had been inspired by Anne's father, A.E. Miles, who had told him that 'Denmark Road was known by that name and once had a gallows in it'. Denmark Road in Gloucester had been re- named in honour of the marriage in 1863 of Princess Alexandra of Denmark to Albert Edward, Prince of Wales (later King Edward VII). But it is not difficult to imagine the scene in an earlier time when passengers travelling by coach out of Gloucester along the

London Road towards the capital would espy a gibbet atop
Wotton Pitch at the junction with Gallows Lane:

> A body adorning
> > Midsummer morning—
> > > An awful warning
> > > > To obey the laws and be good.

E.R.P. Berryman died in 1964, and a further twenty years
were to pass before efforts were made to republish a standard
edition of his rhymes. Both the 1954 and 1960 editions
had run through several reprints before the possibility of
producing more was thwarted by rising costs. In 1971,
Longsmith Books of Gloucester published a large-format,
limited de luxe edition, with calligraphy and illustrations by
Noreen Littleton. But in 1984, Félicité Nesham gave the
copyright in the rhymes, which she had inherited from her
father, to the Gloucestershire Special Adventure Playground,
founded in 1982 in the village of Seven Springs on the A436
road near Cheltenham. The adventure playground is still
there but its name has been changed to the Hop Skip & Jump
Play and Support Centre. Hop Skip & Jump provides day
care facilities and supervised play for children and young
people with physical, emotional and learning difficulties, and
a safe haven where they can play happily and have fun, giving
their parents some much needed respite. It is a registered
charity and is entirely self-supporting.

In her Introduction to the 1984 edition of the rhymes,
reprinted in aid of the Adventure Playground, Felicité wrote
that:

It seemed to me to be something he would have done himself. 'I don't want to make money out of them,' he used to say. 'If they give a little pleasure to people I shall be satisfied.'

There is, however, more to it than that. I won't say 'he loved children' because that is verging on the sentimental. I think he just liked people—I know he did—and he always treated children as special people, never talking down to them, but meeting them on their own uncomplicated levels. Allowing his small grandson to climb up to his shoulders as he sat in his armchair he said, as if it explained everything: 'I'm Everest—William is being Hillary.'

He was, I realise, an Adventure Playground in himself. He built the house-in-a-tree and made small ladders so that we could climb into it—or anywhere else, such as the hollow oak—safely; he organised bicycle sports on the lawn, which made my mother look the other way, and he made what we called 'contraptions' from old toy cars, perambulators, whatever: one, I remember, was steered by pulling on the string attached to the right and left front wheels:—fine, until it broke suddenly!

Anyway, a Special Adventure Playground would be something after his own heart and I can do no less than give this one in Gloucestershire the copyright in the 'Rhymes' and cover the printing costs. If he had not been such a gentle and forgiving person I would say that I have a feeling he would haunt me if I didn't!

Charles Lee Williams expressed a similar sentiment in the

Foreword to the 1931 edition of his musical settings. 'May I venture to suggest', he wrote, 'that at some future date these "Nursery Rhymes" might be included in an annual "Children's Concert" given perhaps for the benefit of the "Children's Hospital" or some institution that would appreciate a useful and cheery effort made by the school children of Gloucester for their little brothers and sisters'.

That was written long before the introduction of the National Health Service, of course. But there can surely be no doubt that both Ted Berryman, comforter of the small French girl from the shipwreck of the *SS Persia* and Everest for his grandson's Hillary, and Charles Lee Williams would both have considered it entirely appropriate that income from the sale of this latest edition of the rhymes should again be used to benefit the children and young people for whom Hop Skip and Jump provides so much valuable support.

Anthony Boden
September 2008

E.R.P. Berryman

OLD GLOUCESTER

Cathedral

RIVER SEVERN

WESTGATE STREET

BEARLAND

ST JOHN'S

NORTHGATE STREET

HARE LANE

ST ALDATE

OXBODE

BARBICAN

BULL LANE

LADYBELLEGATE

LONGSMITH

BLACKFRIARS

EASTGATE STREET

KING'S STREET

DOG LANE

CLARENCE STREET

SOUTHGATE STREET

GREYFRIARS

BELL LANE

Docks

GREEN DRAGON LANE (PARLIAMENT STREET)

BRUNSWICK ROAD

BARTON STREET

Gaudy Green

'As sure as God's in Gloucestershire,'
said they who long ago
Walked closely with Him hereabouts,
and surely they would know:
They found Him at their homely tasks,
they met Him by the way;
Let us make sure, as they made sure,
that He is here today.

To Him the old ones brought their cares,
to Him the young ones prayed,
Through Him the broadcast seed bore fruit,
by Him was sickness stayed;
They sensed Him everywhere they went,
by stream, by tree, and hill,
Let us make sure, as they made sure,
that He is with us still.

E.R.P. Berryman

I

The Gates of Gloucester

Who takes the road from Northgate
   And climbs by Birdlip Down
Will tramp the road the Romans made
   To Cirencester town.
And Southgate leads you seaward,
   Where masted schooners ride
Into the heart of Bristol town
   On Avon's lazy tide.

From Eastgate to the Beacon,
   Behind a drifting cloud
The road climbs up by Painswick Hill
   And tumbles into Stroud.
From Westgate's ancient highway
   Through orchard-laden vales
You'll pass by Ross and Hereford
   And all the way to Wales.

II
Deans Walk

Oh, Canons canter and Rectors ride,
  Vicars vary from stroll to stalk—
But Deans, oh Deans are so dignified
  For a Dean will always walk.

III

Miller's Green

The heavy round mill-stones they grind up the corn
And the miller is hard at his work with the dawn,
Collecting the silvery flour into sacks,
Oh! the miller must have the most aching of backs!
No rest for the miller from morning till night,
By the end of the day he is powder'd all white.

But when Saturday comes the miller will run
With his wife and his children to join in the fun,
To dance round the may-pole and breathe the fresh air
And watch folk enjoying the fun of the fair.
Miller's white while he works, but none's smarter I ween
Than the miller at play down on broad Miller's Green.

IV

Oxbode Lane*

There's an ox lying dead at the end of the lane,
His head on the pathway, his feet in the drain,
The lane is so narrow, his back was so wide,
He got stuck in the road 'twixt a house on each side.

He couldn't go forward, he couldn't go back,
He was stuck just as tight as a nail in a crack,
And the people all shouted, 'So tightly he fits
We must kill him and carve him and move him in bits.'

So a butcher despatched him and then had a sale
Of his ribs and his sirloin, his rump and his tail;
And the farmer he told me. 'I'll never again
Drive cattle to market down Oxbode Lane.'

*Pronounced Oxbody.

V

Dog Lane and Hare Lane

A hare he sat in his cosy form,
  Heigh-ho, catch-as-catch-can,
A dog he lay in the sunshine warm,
  Heigh-ho, scratch-as-scratch-can.
The hare got up and away he went
And the dog he followed hot on the scent
For a hare for dinner was his intent,
  Heigh-ho, catch-as-catch-can.

The hare he hid in a deep dark wood,
  Heigh-ho, catch-as-catch-can;
But the dog couldn't find him, search how he would,
  Heigh-ho, scratch-as-scratch-can.
He searched and he quartered the wood all day
And when it was dark he came away,
And the hare crept back as asleep he lay,
  Heigh-ho, catch-as-catch-can.

This game went on for many a year,
  Heigh-ho, catch-as-catch-can,
But the dog never got his dinner I fear,
  Heigh-ho, scratch-as-scratch-can.
No, the dog he never quite caught the hare,
And they wore out a track in the grass, just where
They ran their daily race, this pair,
  Heigh-ho, catch-as-catch-can.

Yes, they wore out a track by their fruitless chase,
   Heigh-ho, catch-as-catch-can.
And years ago you could see the place,
   Heigh-ho, scratch-as-scratch-can.
And when the first people built Gloucester town
They found the tracks, all muddy and brown,
Where the hare and the dog used to run up and down,
   Heigh-ho, catch-as-catch-can.

'Here's two ready-made lanes for us!' they cried,
   Heigh-ho, catch-as-catch-can,
'We'll build our houses along each side!'
   Heigh-ho, catch-as-catch-can,
'And we'll name them, for it is only fair
To preserve the tale of this ancient pair.
One after the dog and one after the hare!'
   Heigh-ho, catch-as-catch-can.

VI

Bell Lane

'Many years ago there was an old Town Crier called Lane . . . '
Old story.

Ring the bell, ring the bell, ring the bell, Lane!
Ring it twice over, then ring it again!
Ring when there's sunshine, ring when there's rain,
Ring the bell, ring the bell, ring the bell, Lane!

VII

Parliament Street

Parliament Street! Parliament Street!
Is that where the Houses of Parliament meet?
Oh no, I don't think so, I think that's quite wrong,
It's only a street just for going along.

VIII

Green Dragon Lane
(now Parliament Street)

Mother used to say to me
  'When you go to school
Don't go down Green Dragon Lane,
  At least, not as a rule;
For they say that somewhere
  In behind a wall
A big green dragon lives there,
  Scaly tail an' all.'

So I went another way
  Each day to school because
Of what my mother said to me,
  Longer though it was,
Till one day I started home
  Late because of rain,
So I took a short cut
  Up Green Dragon Lane!

And there I saw the Dragon,
  Shiny, green, and tall,
Leaning on a lamp-post,
  Scaly tail an' all.
I was very frightened
  And began to run
Till he smiled and said to me
  'What's the matter, son?

'Come here and have a chat with me,
   I'm a lonely beast
Since long ago I flew here
   From somewhere in the East.
I like to keep an open house
   But no one ever comes.
What about your home work?
   I'm rather good at sums.'

So we sat down together,
   Books upon our knees,
And he did my home work
   With the greatest ease.
And I promised faithfully
   To look him up again,
And always take the short cut
   Along Green Dragon Lane.

I think I must have dreamt it
   For never once again
Did I meet my Dragon
   In Green Dragon Lane.
So I think he must have
   Flown beyond recall,
My green and friendly Dragon,
   Scaly tail an' all!

IX

Barbican Alley

Barbican Alley is narrow and straight,
Barbican Alley leads down to a gate
Which, ever so many years ago,
Was bolted and barred against a foe.

Those broad green fields where you often play
Were the scene of many a fierce affray;
Roundhead and Royalist, peasant and Prince—
But the marks of the struggle have gone long since.

But Barbican Alley is with us still,
And they can picture the scene, who will,
The soldiers marching—the clash of arms—
And the city resounding to wild alarms.

Barbican Alley. What's in a name?
Not much perhaps; but all the same
The echoing pavements surely ring
With the dead romance of a throneless King.

X

Littleworth

'What!' said the King, as he heard the hoofs clatter,
'They've captured the Southgate? Well, that doesn't matter,
That won't worry me or upset my leisure,
It's of such little worth, they can have it with pleasure.'

XI

Bull Lane

Look out! There's a bull got loose in the lane.
    Steady, Sir, don't take your wife there;
Cavorting about like a ballet dancer,
And using his horns like a Bengal Lancer,
    He's having the time of his life there.

He chased a policeman down the lane
    And up into the air he tossed him;
And up to now he hasn't come down,
At least, not anywhere in the town,
    So I'm rather afraid we've lost him.

And the chap in the china shop over there
    Said 'He's turned my place to a shambles:
Every tea-cup broke, not a soup-plate whole,
Every milk-jug smashed, upon my soul
    It's time he finished his gambols!'

They caught him at last by the ring in his nose
    So he won't be at *those* tricks again, Sir,
But he gave the people a terrible fright,
(They've found the policeman, so that's alright)
    And that's why it's called Bull Lane, Sir.

XII

High Cross

Ages and ages ago
A beautiful cross stood here, you know:
It stood for years, till one fine day
Somebody came and took it away.

There's another cross now, not made of stone,
A policeman, who stands there all alone,
In a long white coat, with his arms out—So,
Telling the people which way to go.

XIII

Gaudy Green

(repeat last line)

Put on your frills and flounces,
Your silver-buckled shoes,
For Gloucester town's on holiday
We've got no time to lose.
Of all the pretty lasses
You'll surely be the Queen.
You'll be the fairest at the Fair
Down there on Gaudy Green.

I'll buy a posy for you—
A ribbon for your hat—
A lovely coloured neckerchief,
Or else a china cat.
Don't waste the precious minutes
Let's hurry to the scene,
And join the happy revellers
Down there on Gaudy Green.

XIV

Mop Fair

Do you want a new mop? Do you want a new maid?
A young lady well versed in the tricks of the trade?
Who will dust all your ceilings, your walls and your floors
And polish the stair-case and windows and doors?
Tell me, where can I find such a paragon, where?
Oh, just along Barton Street, down at Mop Fair.

Do you want a new dairy-maid, madam? A dream
Who'll make nice yellow butter and lovely thick cream:
Who will polish each pan till it shines like a star.
Are there really such maids in existence? There are.
Tell me, where can I find such a paragon, where?
Oh, just along Barton Street, down at Mop Fair.

XV

Longsmith Street

Just here two brothers they kept a forge—
  Hammer, hammer, hammer on the anvil:
One was John, and the other one George—
  Hammer, hammer, hammer on the anvil.
One of 'em was long—the other one small
John was the long 'un, over six foot tall,
(They had another brother whose name was Paul,
  But he never hammered on the anvil.)

These two brothers they came to blows,
  Hammer, hammer, hammer on the anvil:
And john hit George with a hammer on the nose,
  Hammer, hammer, hammer on the anvil:
'John,' said George, 'you're acting rough,
I can't help thinking I've had about enough.'
And off he went in a terrible huff
  Leaving John to hammer on the anvil.

So John—long John—carried on without George
  Hammer, hammer, hammer on the anvil:
But he's gone long since, and so has the forge,
  With its hammer, hammer, hammer on the anvil:
And if you're going that way at all,
Doing some shopping or paying a call
You'll see 'Longsmith Street' written on the wall,
  But no one hammers on the anvil.

XVI

Bearland

Before the town of Gloucester
Went spreading far and wide
All sorts of savage animals
Roamed o'er the country side;
And grandmother will tell you
How once a big black bear
Came running down into the town
And carried off the Mayor.

In case this thing might happen
To any future Mayors,
Folk set apart a piece of land
Exclusively for bears;
They said 'Now that is *their* land,
Where no one else may play.'
And so they called it Bearland,
And do so to this day.

XVII

Quay Street

Quay Street, Quay Street,
  There's quite a bunch of Quay Streets,
    There's Upper and there's Lower, and there's
                              just plain The Quay;
And you'll find there is no need to
  Ask policemen where they lead to,
For of course they all lead to the docks, the Severn
                                and the sea.

XVIII

Gallows Lane
(now Denmark Road)

No trace of its murky past
  Is borne on the wind that blows
Down Denmark Road, which now consists
(Or so I see from the agents' lists)
  Of highly respectable
    Very delectable
      What-you'd-expectable
        Houses in orderly rows.

But once at the end of the lane
  A menacing gallows stood,
Where they strung you up if you stole a sheep,
And folk would see as they rose from sleep
  A body adorning
    Midsummer morning—
      An awful warning
        To obey the laws and be good.

But there's nothing like that today,
  Nothing to make you frown;
Clean as a whistle and smart as paint,
Just go and see for yourself if it ain't
  Swept and garnished,
    Polished and varnished,
      Nothing is tarnished,
        The smartest street in town.

XIX

Lady Belle-Gate

Why is it called that name, you ask?
Well, that is a rather difficult task,
I think it must have something to do
With a lady, a bell, and a gate, don't you?
And as it appears that nobody knows
We'll make up a story, and just suppose!

My lady went a-riding
   And went out by the gate,
My lady met her cavalier—
   My lady came home late!
Her father asked the reason why,
   And mightily he swore
That, while he lived, my lady
   Should ride abroad no more.

My lady's lover laughed at him,
   And gave my lady fair
Upon a silken ribbon
   A tiny bell to wear:
My lady bribed a serving-man,
   Whene'er she came back late
To listen for my lady's bell
   And then unbar the gate.

And so they still went riding
  And still they came back late
And when my lady rang her bell
  The big forbidding gate
Was opened for her secretly—
  That's all there is to tell
Of the gate my lady opened
  With her tiny golden bell.

XX

The Friars of Gloucester*

Grey Friars! Grey Friars!
How d'you do today, Friars?
You look so fat and jolly, and your
   laughter sounds so gay.
Yes sir! Quite sir!
What you say is right, sir,
The happiest men in Gloucester
   are the Friars that dress in grey.

* Tunes based upon the chimes of Gloucester cathedral.

E.R.P. Berryman

Black Friars! Black Friars!
Alas and alack Friars!
You look as if you carried all men's
          cares upon your back.
Yes sir! True sir!
We quite agree with you, sir,
The saddest men in Gloucester
          are the Friars that dress in black.

White Friars! White Friars!
What a pretty sight, Friars!
As you file across to vespers in the
golden evening light.
That's, sir, so, sir,
Everybody knows, sir,
The cleanest men in Gloucester
are the Friars that dress in white.

XXI

Port o' Gloucester

See where our shining river runs her winding
                        banks between
Amongst whose shoals and shelving sands
                     in graceful barquantine
Stout-hearted merchant captains steered
                    courageously and sought
A warm west country welcome in old
                  Gloucester's friendly port.

And from the hills at shearing time through
                  rough, deep-rutted vales
The wagoners brought down the wool in
                 bulging tight-packed bales,
For to be shipp'd across the sea and woven
                   in Flemish mills
To bring prosperity and fame to our beloved hills.

(Go, seek those fam'd wool churches that
                  grace our ageless wold,
Built to the glory of the Lord with hard-won
                   yeoman gold;
With love and pride and gratitude each
                 rough-hewn stone was laid
That we who worship there might know
                how well the debt was paid.)

Gone is the tall three-master now,
                    today sleek barges glide
Along a man-made waterway that
                    knows no lock nor tide;
And be it wood or grain or oil,
                    whate'er it is they've brought
A welcome still awaits them there
                    in Gloucester's ancient port.

XXII

Sneedham's Green

Oh, some are Red and some are Blue,
And some are in between;
But one thing that we know is true
Is this—that Sneedham's Green.

XXIII

Upton St Leonards and Painswick

Good folk who live in Upton
   St Leonards do not try
The tempers of the Painswick men
   By shouting 'Bow-wow Pie!'
For they will stand no nonsense
   And scathingly reply,
'Who put a pig upon a wall
   To see the band go by?'

XXIV

Ninety-nine Trees

Are there really ninety and nine yew trees
Round Painswick church? I wonder.
And ninety-nine firs on top of May Hill,
Braving the storms and thunder?
And on May Hill, say the folk who know,
The hundredth fir tree will never grow.

———————

Let's start counting 'em, you and me,
Start at this corner, one—two—three—
Now let's stop and have some tea.

There, tea's finished, let's begin again,
Four, five, six, seven, eight, nine, ten,
When shall we finish? I don't know when.

You'll be all day totting up these trees,
It might be quicker if you counted 'em in threes.
Don't interrupt me while I'm counting, please.

Sixty, sixty-one, two—three—four,
We're getting on fast, not so many more,
Where'd I got to? I've forgotten. Oh Lor'!

Start again here, this'll do fine,
Sixty—What! You make it fifty-nine?
Oh, why is your arithmetic so different from mine?

Eighty—eighty-one, we're nearly through,
But last time I counted 'em this one was eighty-two,
I'm almost sure. Oh dear, what shall I do?

Let's go home and try another day,
Let's start next time round the other way,
Anyhow they've never been counted right, they say.

XXV

Horsepools

In the days gone by when these hills were wild
And your great-great-great-grandfather a child,
All animals had their particular rules
For drinking from rivers and puddles and pools.
You'd not find, for instance, a weasel or stoat
Would drink from the very same place as a goat;
Dogs, donkeys and horses, pigs, cattle and sheep
To their own drinking places would faithfully keep;
They thought it bad manners, in fact quite the worst,
To break with tradition when quenching their thirst.
But that's all over, today you'll find
They all drink together and none of 'em mind,
And all that's survived of the ancient rules
Is the name that has stuck to some old muddy pools
Up there, where the horses used to drink—
At any rate, that's what I like to think.

Maybe there's just one survival more,
That bowl over there, on the kitchen floor
Marked DOG so plainly, to show who it's for.

XXVI

Spoonbed Farm

When old farmer Nuthatch, who lived on the hill,
Departed this life he left in his Will
His horses and haystacks, his geese and his guns,
His poultry and pigs to his two elder sons.

'My youngest son, John, is rather too small
To have any property left him at all:
But to show how I love him I'll leave him,' he said,
'An old silver spoon and my four-poster bed.'

John Nuthatch grew up and worked hard every day
At sowing and reaping and carting the hay:
So industrious was he, by the time he was twenty
He had lots in the bank and savings a-plenty.

So he married a wife who had beauty and charm
And out of his savings he bought a nice farm:
'Spoonbed Farm we will call it: for that's all,' he said
'Father started me off with—a spoon and a bed!'

XXVII

September 5th, 1643

Up on the hill there, all alone,
Just where the road begins to bend,
A King stood silent beside a stone
And thought to himself, 'Is this the end?
Have I failed my people? God knows, I've tried;
He made me a King—let Him decide.'

His horse stood by him with drooping head,
Chest and bridle all flecked with foam,
When his stripling son came up and said
'Father, when are we going home?'
And to the boom of a distant gun,
He answered. 'We have no home, my son.'

And if you go up to Seven Leas Lane
You'll see the spot and the self-same stone
Where a King once stood in the driving rain
And thought of the future, all unknown;
And as he mounted and rode away
It was more than the close of an autumn day.

XXVII

The King's Head, Upton St Leonards

King Henry went a-hunting in the wilds
    of Prinknash Park
And when the shadows lengthened and the
    woods grew cold and dark
The King called off the chase and cried
    'Now find me if you can
Some hostelrie whereat we may refresh
    the inner man!'

Down came King Henry with his Queen,
    the gracious Anne Boleyn,
And with all their gallant company
    they stormed the village inn;
There was eating, there was drinking,
    there were junketings galore,
And when they'd drunk the cellar dry
    they loudly called for more.

The King grew right merry with the
    mellow Cotswold ale,
And slapped mine host upon the back
    and cried (so runs the tale)
'Right royally hast thou served us, sir,
    and I command' he said
'Henceforth this noble hostelrie be dubbed
    The King, Hys Heade!'

Today when huntsmen meet where all this
   merriment took place
And drink a welcome stirrup-cup
   to warm them for the chase
Men say a bluff familiar shade
   his way among them wends
And lifts a ghostly tankard with the cry
   'Good Hunting, friends!'

XXIX

Cooper's Hill

Here once stood a cottage where rabbits now roam
And a couple called Cooper they made it their home;
But that's all disappeared Oh, so long, long ago
And all that is left is a legend or so.

Mrs Cooper was house-proud, she dusted and mopped
Week in and week out, she scarce ever stopped;
So spotless her carpets, so polished each door
You could shave in a panel or dine off the floor.

Old Cooper made cheeses, but 'Oh,' said his wife,
'Those cheeses are truly the bane of my life;
He leaves them on tables, he leaves them on chairs,
And this morning I found a large cheese on the stairs!'

This went on for years, till one day she swore,
'I can stand it no longer, this is the last straw;
Just look at this cheese on my clean window-sill!'
And she gave it a shove and it rolled down the hill.

It whizzed past his head and old Cooper gave chase
And caught it and brought it back safe. 'What a race
That would make for the lads of the village!' he mused,
'Though it's not quite the way I like cheese to be used!'

So that's how it started, and today people flock
Where an elder in top-hat beribbon'd and smock
Sends lads chasing a cheese down the hill-side below
Just like old Mister Cooper did long, long ago.

XXX

The Fiddler's Elbow

Do you see the scar on the far hill-side,
Where they've made the roadway broad and wide?
It wasn't always like that, you know,
In the happy-go-lucky long ago.

You see where the hill-side flattens out,
It was there that the folk from roundabout
Would gather and set aside their cares
And dance to a fiddler's homely airs.

He'd play till the moon rose over the rim
Of the beacon yonder—no rest for him:
He'd play till the light of dawn first showed.
And the dancers took their homeward road.

He played until he was ninety-four,
Then his arm grew stiff and he played no more,
And he died. 'Alas!' all the people said,
'How shall we dance now our fiddler's dead?'

And the road that runs by the side of the hill,
They call it the Fiddler's Elbow still—
It's bent like the fiddler's arm was—so—
In the happy-go-lucky long ago.

XXXI

Painswick Beacon

How much unwritten history
  Lies hid beneath your turf,
Amid the long-forgotten bones
  Of warrior and of serf;
How often round your deep-dug trench
  The noise of battle rang,
The well-aimed blow of sword or spear,
  The shield's resounding clang.

And did men light a signal-fire
  By western breezes fanned
To spread the news of victory
  Through all the waiting land?
The fire that leapt from peak to peak
  Across this anxious isle
Till far-off Skiddaw's glare aroused
  The burghers of Carlisle.

The rebel and the Royalist
  Have trod your gentle slopes,
Your grass-grown battlements have been
  The grave of shatter'd hopes;
And once a brave, unhappy King
  Robbed of his royal power
Undaunted rode across your brow
  To meet his destined hour.

XXXII

Hucclecote Ball

Oh! get out my lovely gold button-and-buckle coat
For there's going to be a grand party at Hucclecote.
For Knights will be there with their squires and their dames,
There'll be eating and drinking and dancing and games;
Lord Badger Brockworth will be there, of course,
He's a Knight of the Garter and Master of Horse;
And Baroness Birdlip whose son, as you know,
Married Count Cranham's daughter two summers ago.
The Laird of Longlevens in sporran and kilt,
With his coronet dashingly worn at a tilt;
Sir Robinswood Hill will no doubt take the floor,
And Sir Framilode Severn, a terrible bore.
They'll come from the length and the breadth of the land,
From Glasgow to Gloucester, from Stroud to the Strand.
Viscount Upton St Leonards is sure to be there,
With Lord Peter Painswick, his young son and heir.
Dukes, Duchesses, Baronets, Countesses, Earls,
Diamonds and sapphires, and opals and pearls,
Worn by the bluest of blue in the land.
What a wonderful party, and won't it be grand!
Sir Hartpury Horsepools, booted and spurred
(He says he's descended from Richard the Third).
And the Duchess of Duntisbourne Abbotts, I hope,
Will be there, and the Bishop in mitre and cope;
And Lady Leckhampton, her daughters and sons,
All the big noises and all the big guns.
Earl Edge and his brother, Sir Jericho Pitch,

(They're twins, I can never tell 'tother from which);
The Marquess of Matson, the Earl of Northleach,
(If he gets half a chance he'll make a long speech);
The Duke of Down Hatherley—crutches and all—
And the Duchess who thinks she'll be belle of the ball.
There's no end to the wonderful names on the list,
It's a party most certainly not to be missed:

so

Get out my lovely gold button-and-buckle coat
I *must* go to this wonderful party at Hucclecote!

XXXIII

Robins Wood Hill

Each year the Great King Robin
　　Sends out his Royal word
(I think it's in December,
　　About the twenty-third)
'To all my subject Robins
　　Greetings, and be so good
As to assemble secretly
　　To-night in Robins' Wood!'

But you will never find it,
　　However hard you search—
That little legendary wood
　　Of spruce and silver birch
Where Robins old and Robins young
　　In all their bright array
Gather to get their King's commands,
　　Each one, for Christmas Day.

'Rees farm for you!' he orders one
　　'And you to Edmonds Hill!
And don't forget to hop about
　　Along the window-sill—
And you—to Amberley: and you
　　Away to Miller's Green
And wish a Merry Christmas to
　　His Reverence the Dean!'

XXXIV

Matson Pitch

Careful, Joe! Or you'll be in the ditch.
There's always a dog on Matson Pitch.
His great-great-great-grandfather lay
Just about here in the heat of day,
And it's bred in the bone for a dog to lie
Where his forefathers did in the days gone by.
Ah! Those were the days of long ago
When the fastest traffic went parlous slow,
And about the speediest thing of the lot
Was the baker's cart, at a slow jog trot.
Plenty of time for the dog who lay
Fast asleep in the King's highway
To rise and walk to the roadside grass,
Or to lie quite still and let it pass.
And you may sound your horn as you will
But that dog won't budge—not an inch—until
He feels inclined, he may even bide
And make you pass on the other side.
'My great-great-grandfather used to lie
Just here and let the world go by,'
He says to himself, 'so why can't I?'
    Careful Joe! Or you'll be in the ditch,
    There's always a dog on Matson Pitch.

XXXV

Up Hatherley and Down Hatherley

There are two little villages close to the town,
One of 'em's Up and the other one's Down;
And once on a time a sprite, so they say,
Used to tell people wrong when asking the way.
                    Hitherley-hatherley
                        Ditherley-datherley
    Mind who you ask when you're asking the way!

You'd meet an old fellow all wrinkled and brown
And ask him the best way to Hatherley (Down),
And later you'd know that he'd sold you a pup
For you'd find yourself making for Hatherley (Up).

Or perhaps 'twould be dressed in another disguise,
A charming young lady with pretty blue eyes,
And she'd smilingly say to a stranger from town
'*That's* the way to Up Hatherley', pointing to Down.

All this of course happened a long time ago
And you ask if it's true, well, I really don't know.
But such things don't happen to people today
For lovely white sign-posts will show them the way.
                    Hitherley-hatherley
                        Ditherley-datherley
    Mind who you ask when you're asking the way!

XXXVI

Summer Song

The swallows come to Ullenwood
  And go away too soon,
Before the browning woods are kiss'd
By little swirls of autumn mist
  Up by the Air Balloon.

The nightingales in Ullenwood
  Still sing their age-old tune,
Just as they did when Legions tramp'd
The rule-straight Roman roads and camp'd
  Up by the Air Balloon.

Across the slopes of Ullenwood
  Beneath a waning moon
They tell of ghosts that walk again,
Briton and Roman, Norman, Dane,
  Up by the Air Balloon.

I think I'll go to Ullenwood
  This very afternoon,
To hear the click of bat on ball,
The white-clad umpire's drowsy call,
  Up by the Air Balloon.

XXXVII

The Windrush

As a restless young trout I meandered about
Lithe, lissom, impatient and active:
I was born in the Ouse, and I wanted to choose
A stream with a name more attractive.

The one I have found suits me down to the ground,
(Or should I say 'down to the sand'?)
Where the winds gently sigh, and the rushes reply
On the loveliest stream in the land.

XXXVIII

Standish Church

God gave to man this spreading vale
   In which to take his pride,
Fair heritage of hill and dale
   From Stroud to Severn tide;
And man his love and labour lent—
   His craftsmanship—to build
This slender spire, a monument
   To grace the fields he till'd.

Across the spring-clad quickening wold
   And summer's landscape bright,
Down autumn's patchwork, green and gold,
   And winter's robe of white,
The bells that our forefathers pealed
   In those forgotten days
Still summon us from farm and field
   To precept and to praise.

Six hundred long-drawn years have died
   And still their memories live
Who built with such ungrudging pride
   And all they had to give:
Let all the world be out of joint
   And faith, like Homer, nod,
That lonely, lovely pencil-point
   Still shows the way to God.

XXXIX

Seven Springs

This little tale I tell to you
Is all about a kangaroo,
A much admired marsupial who
Escaped one day from Clifton Zoo
In April, eighteen-eighty-two.
I wonder if it's really true?

The Kangaroo was bored to tears
Being caged up for years and years,
She could not stand the rows of faces
That stared and grinned and made grimaces,
The crowds that by her cage would slouch
And made remarks about her pouch.
And one fine day she said 'A-ha!
The keeper's left the door ajar!'
She crept outside and looked around.
'There'll be a row if I am found
Outside.' She said, 'I'd better hop it
Before—excuse my slang—I cop it!'
And suddenly there was a shout
'Beware! The kangaroo is out!'
She sprang, and sailed across the sky
And landed close to Ross-on-Wye,
But being frightened by the crowd
She sprang again to land in Stroud.
Finding it uncongenial there

She sprang to Weston-super-Mare.
Good folk out shopping stood and gaped
And yelled 'The kangaroo's escaped!'
The keepers called into their aid
Policemen and the fire brigade.
'Chase her and bring her back!' they cried
As they rushed round the countryside.
'This ain't,' the kangaroo remarked,
'A very safe place to be parked.
Besides I think it's going to rain,
I'd best be on the move again.'
She sprang and hid behind a hedge
Not far from Wotton-under-Edge,
And there she rested, not for long,
For the pursuit was hot and strong.
Again she sprang and landed, roughly,
About a mile this side of Tuffley.
But they were hot upon her track,
'Catch her!' they cried, 'and bring her back!'
She sprang once more, and none too soon,
And landed near the Air Balloon.
But she was tiring now, and so
She hardly knew which way to go.
Pursuers rushed up Crickley Hill
Like hounds all eager for the kill.
And so her final spring she took
And landed in a little brook

Where her pursuers later found her
And with some string they gently bound her,
And to the Zoo took her away
Where you can see her any day.

————————

Thus seven springs in all she took
And that is why the little brook
Is known as Seven Springs today.
But there are people who will say
That's not the reason, but the brook
Has seven springs—and if you look
You'll see seven springs I know
From which the Thames begins to flow.
But I don't think that's true, and I
Have told you what's the reason why.
Undoubtedly the name is due
To our old friend, the Kangaroo.

XL

Rhyme of a Seven Springer

There's some as votes
A spring at Coates
Is where ole Thames begins:
But them's a fraud,
And may the Lord
Forgive 'em for their sins!

For us all claims
That Father Thames
From Severn Springs starts flowin',
And them smart chaps
As makes the maps
Well, how would they be knowin'?

Us says a stream
So it would seem
Should have some water in 'un:
But how can one
That ain't got none
Be old man Thame's beginnun'?

XLI

Cotswold Tiles

The finest roofs in all the land are made from Cotswold stone,
And the mason gives each tile a name like children of his own.
By length and breadth the tally runs, by width and depth and
size,
And the mason knows them all by name, for he is very wise.

Long Day, Short Day, Moreday and Muffity,
  Lye-byes and Bottomers, each a name receives:
Wivett, Beck, and Cussomes, Cutting, Third and Bachelor,
  Smallest under roof-ridge, largest over eaves.

Each tile in its own special place is hung with loving care.
And they weather down the ages in the mellow Cotswold air:
Twenty-six in all there are—the family's not small,
I can but tell you one or two, I can't remember all.

Long Day, Short Day, Moreday and Muffity,
  Lye-byes and Bottomers, each a name receives:
Wivett, Beck, and Cussomes, Cutting, Third and Bachelor,
  Smallest under roof-ridge, largest over eaves.

E.R.P. Berryman

XLII

The Severn Bore

When primitive man in his coracle queer
Went fishing for eels at the turn of the year
Down Minsterworth way he suddenly saw
A mighty big wave rushing up-stream—The Bore!

He knew all about eels and how you should catch 'em,
And primitive dwellings and how you should thatch 'em,
And how to catch mammoths and tan their thick hides,
But he didn't know much about spring and neap tides.

'Are the River Gods angry?' he cried in dismay:
'Did I mumble my prayers at the temple today?
Will they drown me for not having done what I should?'
And he made for the bank just as fast as he could.

He jumped out and ran up the bank for his life
And shouted 'Look out!' to his primitive wife—
'The Gods of the River are angry indeed,
They've just tried to drown me, but didn't succeed!'

Just then with a rip and a rush and a roar
The on-coming wave swept by close to their door,
And they both stood there shivering, frighten'd to death,
Hardly daring to blink or to take a deep breath.

Then the water subsided, and they got very brave
And went hand-in-hand to a neighbouring cave,
Where the River Gods lived, and as they got near
He said, 'We must sacrifice something, my dear.'

So he stooped and he fumbled about in his creel
And pulled out the longest and juiciest eel.
'This creature,' he said, 'I think ought to appease 'em,
There's no doubt we've got to do something to please 'em.'

So he boiled it in milk and he fried it in fat
And put it just there on a primitive mat,
And never again, no, never more
Was he caught catching eels by the Terrible Bore!

XLIII

Pax Romana

The Romans came to Gloucestershire
  And found it very fair,
They built a town within a wall
  And left a legion there;
And all our hills brought back to them
  Fond memories of home,
Their own fair city founded on
  The seven hills of Rome.

The Romans stayed in Gloucestershire
  For full four hundred years,
And generations came and went
  With all their hopes and fears;
They saw our dawns rise through the mist,
  Our sunsets glow and fade,
The old unchanging loveliness
  Of Cotswold light and shade.

The Romans sped from Gloucestershire
  To stay the Vandal horde,
And all the land they learnt to love
  Was put to fire and sword;
And only those who dig and delve
  In Cotswold clay and loam
Find traces of those far off days—
  The legacy of Rome.

A villa's gay mosaic floor
  Deep down beneath some farm,
An ornament that once had graced
  A Roman maiden's arm;
A broken bowl—a buried wall—
  But something more than these
The Romans left behind—their love
  Of order, law, and peace.

XLIV

Sign-posts

You meet a yokel on the road
   And ask of him the way,
He'll answer 'I'm a stranger 'ere,
I've only been 'ere twenny year
   So I can't rightly say!'

But sign-posts are so sensible,
   They always seem to know;
All painted nice and clean and white
With arms that point to left and right
   And tell you where to go.

'It's twenty miles' the sign-post says
   'To Stow-upon-the-Wold;
'Or if this road you'd like to try
It's ten to Ross-upon-the-Wye,
   A pleasant trip I'm told!'

A hundred miles to London Town!
   That's not the way for me!
I'll take this one to Upton Hill,
Six miles it says, and so I will
   Be home in time for tea.